LEGO® STAR WARS™

BATTLE FOR THE STOLEN CRYSTALS

CONTENTS

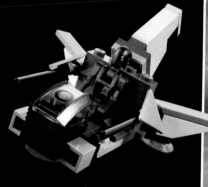

THE CLONE WARS

For centuries the galaxy was a place of peace, harmony, and justice, but now it has been plunged into war. Mysterious dark forces threaten the Republic, which must fight for its survival.

THE REPUBLIC

On one side of the Clone Wars is the Republic and its clone army. Life in the Republic was peaceful until the Separatists suddenly attacked it. The clone army has taken up arms to fight for democracy and to protect all the planets in the Republic from the invading Separatists.

GALACTIC SENATE

The Republic is ruled by the Galactic Senate, which is led by Chancellor Palpatine. The Republic is democratic: Every planet elects a politician to represent them in the Senate.

THE JEDI

The Jedi Council is the ruling body of the Jedi Order and is led by Grand Master Yoda. The Jedi have always been peacekeepers in the galaxy, but now they have been forced to become generals and lead the clone army.

THE CLONE ARMY

The clone army is made up of millions of clone troopers from the planet Kamino. They are human clones who have been specially bred to be soldiers. The clone troopers are obedient and are trained to follow orders without question.

Clone Commander Gree is a leader in the clone army.

SITH LORD

Few realize it, but the Sith Lord Darth Sidious controls the Separatists. He is a master of the dark side who wants to take over the galaxy. His second-in-command is Count Dooku.

THE SEPARATISTS

On the other side of the Clone Wars are the Separatists. They have attacked the Republic and are terrorizing the galaxy with their droid army. The group of breakaway planets and organizations is led by a mysterious figure who craves absolute power over everyone.

SEPARATIST ALLIANCE

The Separatist Alliance is a group of greedy politicians and merchants. They think that the Clone Wars will make them more rich and powerful, but really they are just pawns of Darth Sidious.

THE DROID ARMY

The Separatists have created a metal army to fight on their behalf. It is made up of different types of battle droids. They are droids who have only simple programming and so cannot think for themselves.

Commando droids serve Count Dooku in the droid army.

DATA FILE

NAME: Clone Commander Gree (designation 1004)
SPECIES: Human (cloned)
ROLE: Leader of the 41st Elite Corps of Clone Troopers, member of the 9th Assault Corps
WEAPON: DC-15 blaster rifle
HOMEWORLD: Kamino
AFFILIATION: The Republic

Meet Commander Gree! Like all clone soldiers in the Grand Army of the Republic, he was cloned on Kamino and bred to be a warrior. During the Clone Wars he is a loyal and disciplined soldier who serves as second-in-command to Jedi General Luminara Unduli.

Black visor

Bandolier

Blast-proof white armor

Black body glove under armor

Utility belt

Black gloves

LEADER

Gree excelled as a cadet on Kamino and so was selected for an advanced program. He was trained in leadership and decision-making and is now a senior commander. Unlike ordinary clone troopers, he can think for himself so is suited for solo missions.

CAMOUFLAGE

Gree wears phase I clone trooper armor with green markings. It is particularly useful for missions to planets like Kashyyyk, where he blends into the lush jungle surroundings.

COMMANDO DROID

DATA FILE

NAME: Commando Droid
TYPE: BX-series Battle Droid
ROLE: Stealth assignments
WEAPON: E-5 blaster rifle
HOMEWORLD: Geonosis
AFFILIATION: The Separatists

Watch out for commando droids! They may look like ordinary battle droids, but they are far more deadly. These superior droids are tougher, stronger, and faster and have more sophisticated programming than the basic B1 model of battle droid.

SPECIAL OPS

Commando droids' complexity makes them more expensive to produce so they are reserved for only the most critical missions. Their advanced thinking processes and superior strength make them particularly suited to stealth activity.

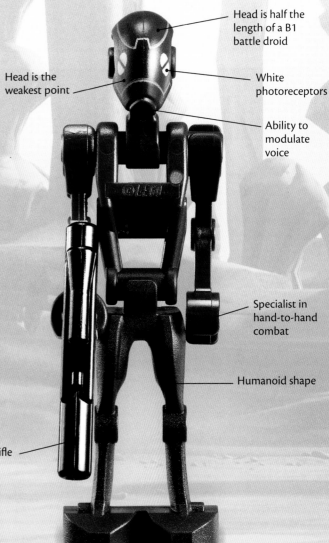

Head is half the length of a B1 battle droid

Head is the weakest point

White photoreceptors

Ability to modulate voice

Specialist in hand-to-hand combat

Humanoid shape

E-5 blaster rifle

ELITE DROID

Commando droids are very agile, despite their heavy armor. Their advanced programming means they can think fast and adapt to changing situations so they do not just follow orders like ordinary battle droids.

BATTLE IN THE CANYONS

V-19 TORRENT VS. SEPARATIST CANNON

CLONE COMMANDER GREE IS DOING BATTLE IN A CANYON. BUT NOT FOR MUCH LONGER... HE IS ABOUT TO RECEIVE A DIFFERENT MISSION FROM THE JEDI TEMPLE...

CHARGE, MEN!

YODA APPEARS VIA HOLOTRANSMISSION...

MASTER YODA! YOU HAVE NEW ORDERS FOR ME?

YES, COMMANDER GREE. FOR YOU A MISSION, I HAVE. A DROID, YOU MUST SEEK...

...TWO BARRELS OF LIGHTSABER CRYSTALS, STOLEN A DROID HAS.

TAKE THEM OFF-WORLD, HE WILL. WAITING IN THE ICE MOUNTAINS FOR HIM, A SPACECRAFT IS.

OK, CHIEF! I'LL GET THE CRYSTALS BACK!

FAR AWAY THE ICE MOUNTAINS ARE. THROUGH THE FOREST AND ACROSS THE DESERT, GO YOU MUST.

YODA ARRANGES A BRICK DROP SO GREE CAN BUILD A CRAFT TO CHASE AFTER THE DROID.

MASTER YODA DOESN'T WASTE ANY TIME!

OK, TIME TO GET BUILDING!

GREE BUILDS A V-19 TORRENT STARFIGHTER AND FLIES OFF!

NOW READ ABOUT THE **V-19 TORRENT** AND BUILD YOUR OWN! THE ADVENTURE CONTINUES ON **PAGE 22**.

V-19 TORRENT

The V-19 is a fast starfighter with powerful weapons, which makes it a good choice for an attack mission. Plus, if you are headed into danger, it is well armored but still lightweight enough to dodge enemy fire easily.

HYPERSPACE TRAVEL

To travel faster than the speed of light, spacecraft need a hyperdrive. Many ships have to connect to an external hyperdrive, but the V-19 has its own drive built in. Perfect for a quick escape!

Extended S-foil in flight mode

Cockpit

S-FOILS

The V-19 has three S-foils—wings that change position for different maneuvers. The central wing rotates around the back of the cockpit. The side wings fold upward for takeoff and landing in tight spaces. When the wings are wide, the laser cannons on their tips have maximum range.

LANDING POSITION

FLIGHT POSITION

Ion-powered engines

Laser cannon

Central wing in flight position

SPEED
RANGE
ARMOR
FIREPOWER
DEFENSE

DATA FILE

NAME: V-19 Torrent Starfighter
CLASS: Starfighter
TOP SPEED: Faster than the speed of light
ARMAMENT: Two laser cannons, two missile launchers
ROLE: Head-on combat
CREW: One pilot/gunner
AFFILIATION: The Republic

V-19 TORRENT

The nifty V-19 Torrent starfighter is made up of four sections: the cockpit and three S-foils. You can change the position of the S-foils between flight mode and takeoff and landing mode.

1

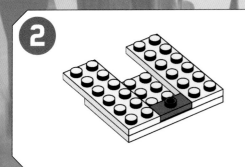

2

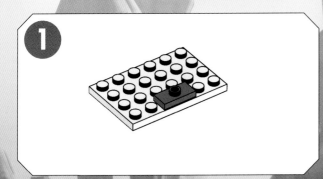

1

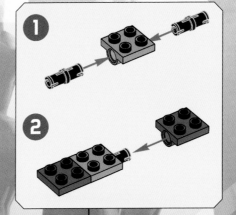

2

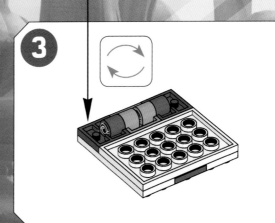

3

4

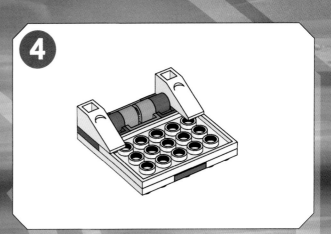

Turn the page to complete the model.

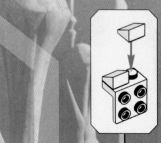

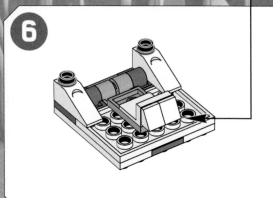

THIS SHIP IS SO FAST, I'LL CATCH THAT CLANKER IN NO TIME!

TOP TIP

Make sure you follow the arrows closely when building the smaller parts of the models.

SPEEDY STARFIGHTER

8

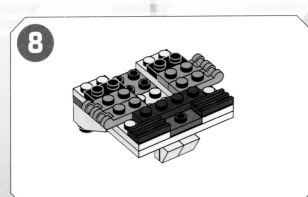

9

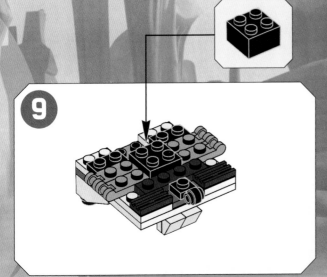

10

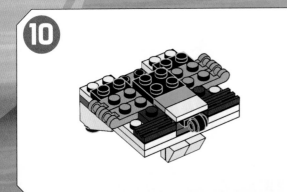

11

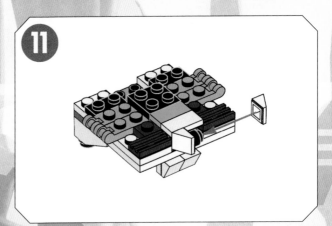

12

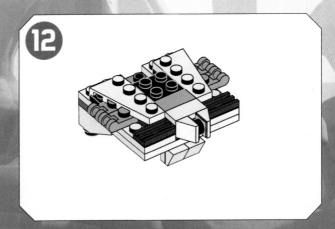

13

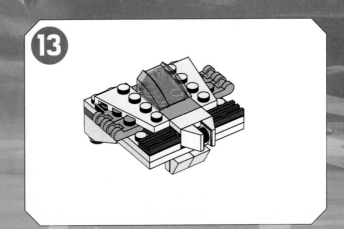

Turn the page to complete the model.

CENTRAL WING

14

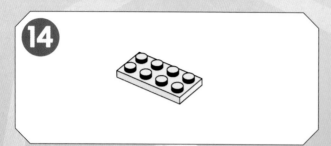

15

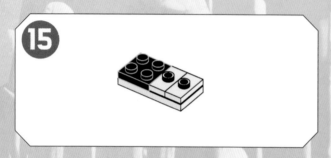

16

17

18

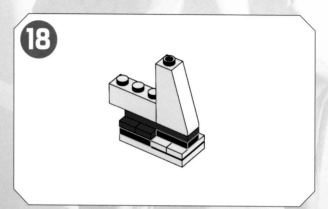

19

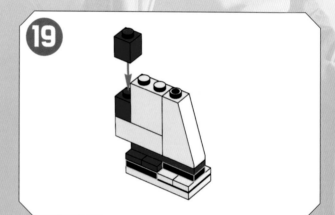

20

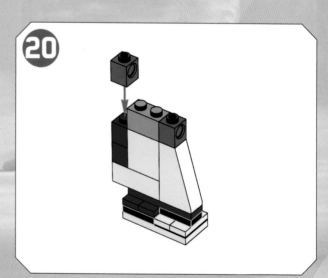

21

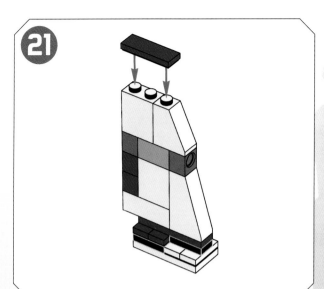

22

23

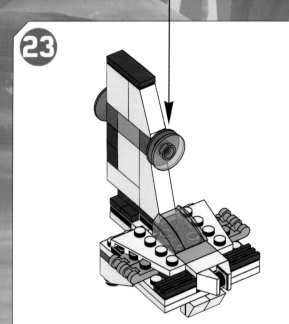

I CAN'T WAIT TO GET BEHIND THOSE CONTROLS!

Turn the page to complete the model.

LEFT WING

24

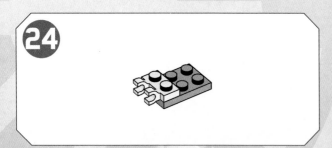

25

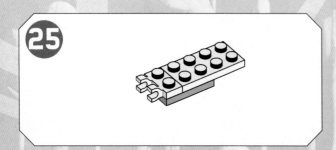

26

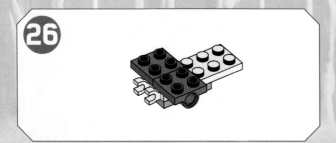

27

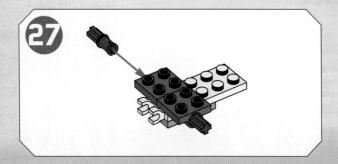

28

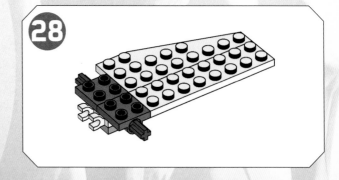

29

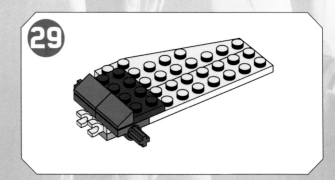

30

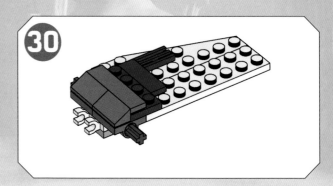

31

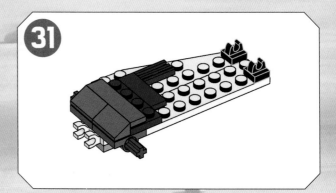

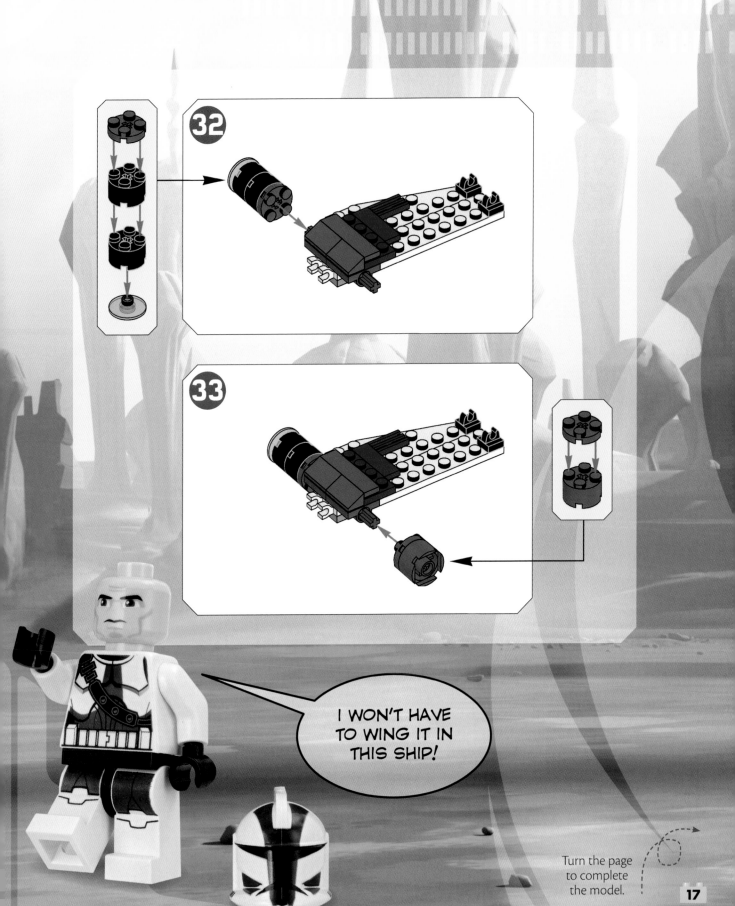

I WON'T HAVE TO WING IT IN THIS SHIP!

Turn the page to complete the model.

THREE WINGS ARE BETTER THAN TWO!

34

35

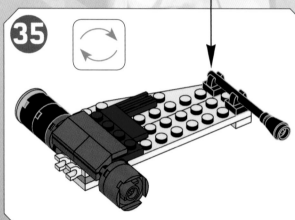

DID YOU KNOW?

The V-19 was first made by the Verpine, who are a species of insect. The ship's controls had to be redesigned so humans could use them.

36

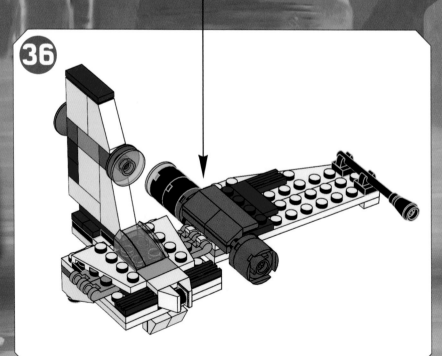

RIGHT WING

37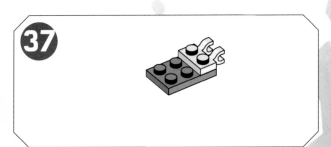

38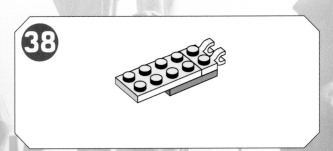

39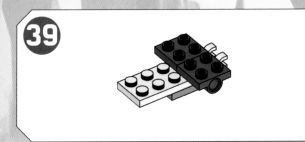

40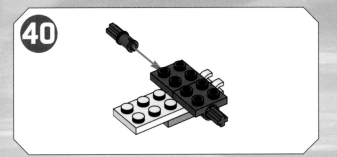

41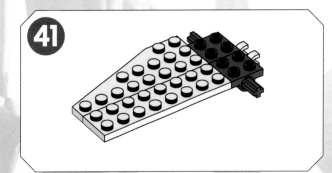

42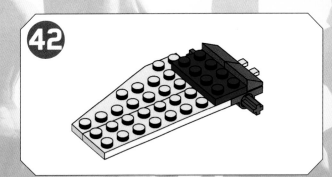

43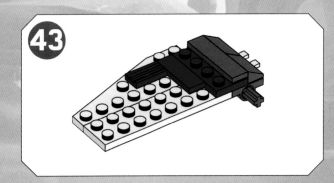

44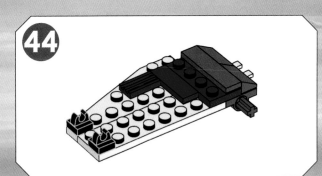

Turn the page to complete the model.

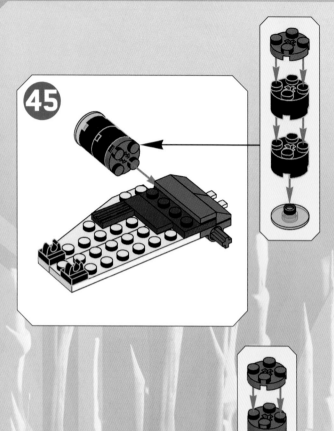

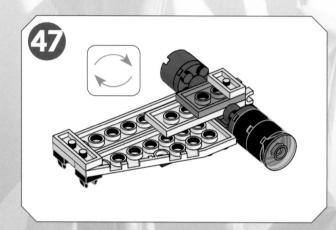

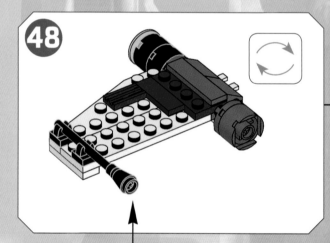

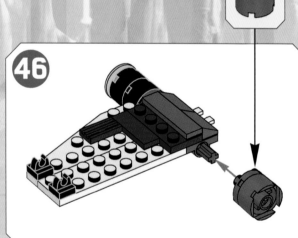

WATCH OUT FOR MY LASER CANNONS, CLANKER!

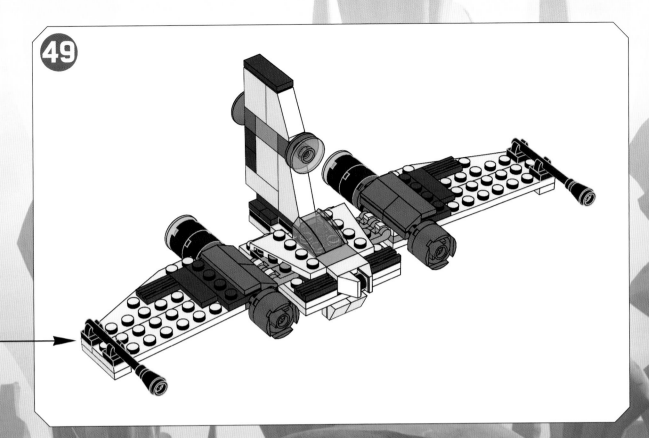

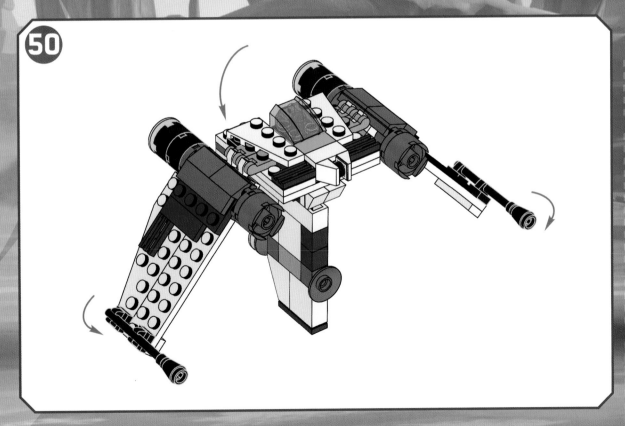

DROID DEFENSE

MEANWHILE, DEEP IN THE CANYON, THE COMMANDO DROID RECEIVES A DATA TRANSMISSION...

INCOMING WARNING: V-19 STARFIGHTER APPROACHING!

THE REPUBLIC WILL NEVER FIND THEIR CRYSTALS! I'VE HIDDEN THEM IN THE DESERT AND SOON I'LL TAKE THEM FAR AWAY!

BUT IN THE MEANTIME, I KNOW JUST WHAT TO BUILD!

CANNON COMPLETED!

TIME TO TEACH YOU NOT TO STEAL, DROID!

THE COMMANDO DROID MOVES HIS CANNON INTO POSITION.

THIS WILL STOP YOU, CLONE!

NOW LEARN ABOUT THE **SEPARATIST CANNON** AND BUILD YOUR OWN! THE ADVENTURE CONTINUES ON **PAGE 30**.

SEPARATIST CANNON

Beware this deadly cannon! It fires proton shells that pick off starfighters like flies. They can also break through deflector shields and bring down the largest assault ships, even when they are miles above the battlefield.

Armored paneling

Barrel

Articulated legs

Cabin for droid operator

Optical sensors

Triangular feet for stability

DATA FILE

NAME: Separatist cannon

CLASS: Artillery

TOP SPEED: 50 kph (30 mph)

ARMAMENT: Proton shells

ROLE: Anti-infantry, anti-aircraft

CREW: One droid operator

AFFILIATION: The Separatists

SPEED
RANGE
ARMOR
FIREPOWER
DEFENSE

TARGETING

The heavily armored cannon is sturdy and stable. It can move its barrel and walk on its four hinged legs, but only very slowly. This limits its ability to hit small, fast-moving targets.

GROUND TARGETS   AERIAL TARGETS

SEPARATIST CANNON

This fearsome cannon consists of two main parts: the barrel and the legs. They are each built with a hinge piece and are joined by connecting the hinge together.

5

1
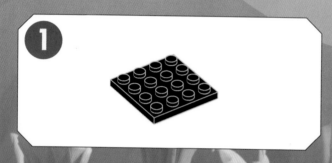

6
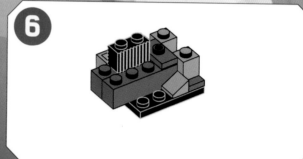

2

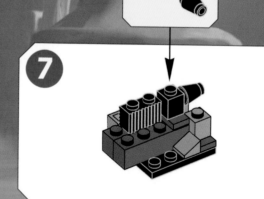

7

3

4

8
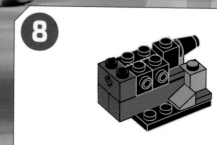

12

9

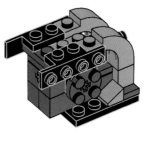

13

10

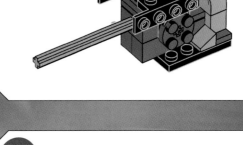

14

11

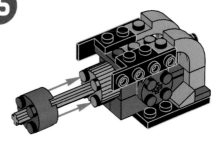

15

Turn the page to complete the model.

DID YOU KNOW?

The Separatists use many types of walking weapons in battle. These include spider droids, dwarf spider droids, and octuptarra combat tri-droids.

18

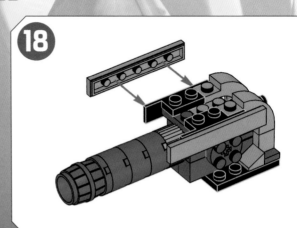

16

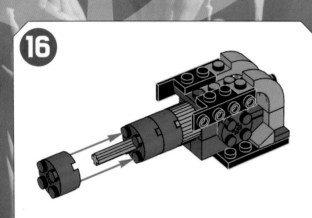

19

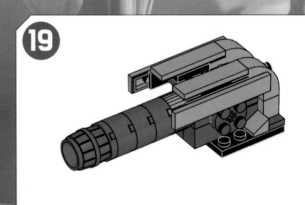

17

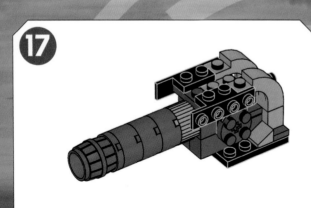

NOTHING CAN STAND IN THE WAY OF THIS CANNON!

CANNON LEGS

1

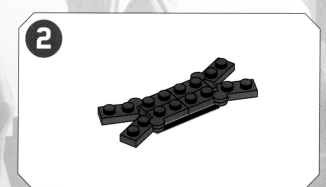

2

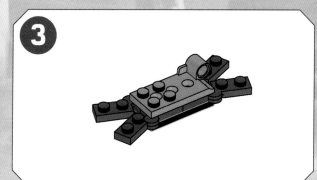

3

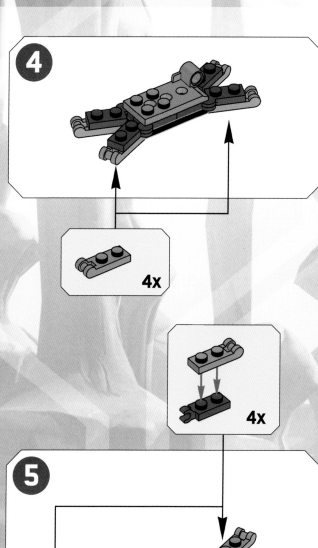

4

4x

4x

5

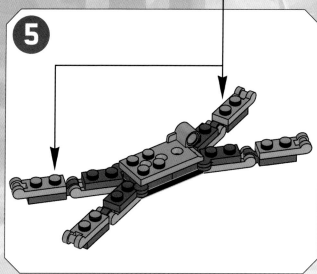

SLOW AND STEADY

Turn the page to complete the model.

READY, AIM, FIRE!

6

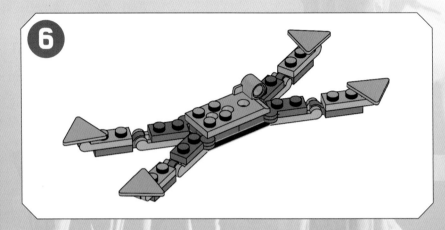

7

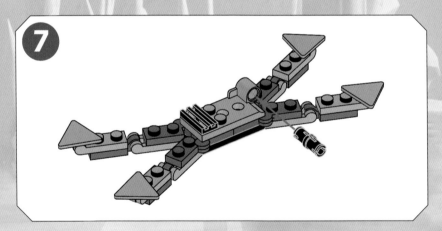

8

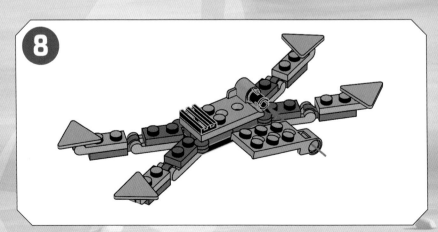

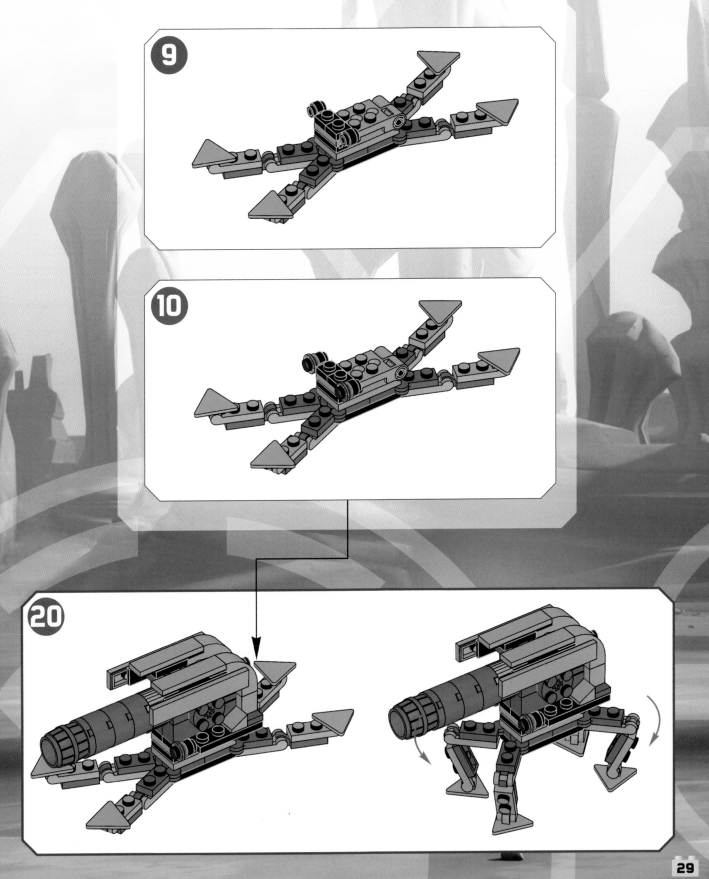

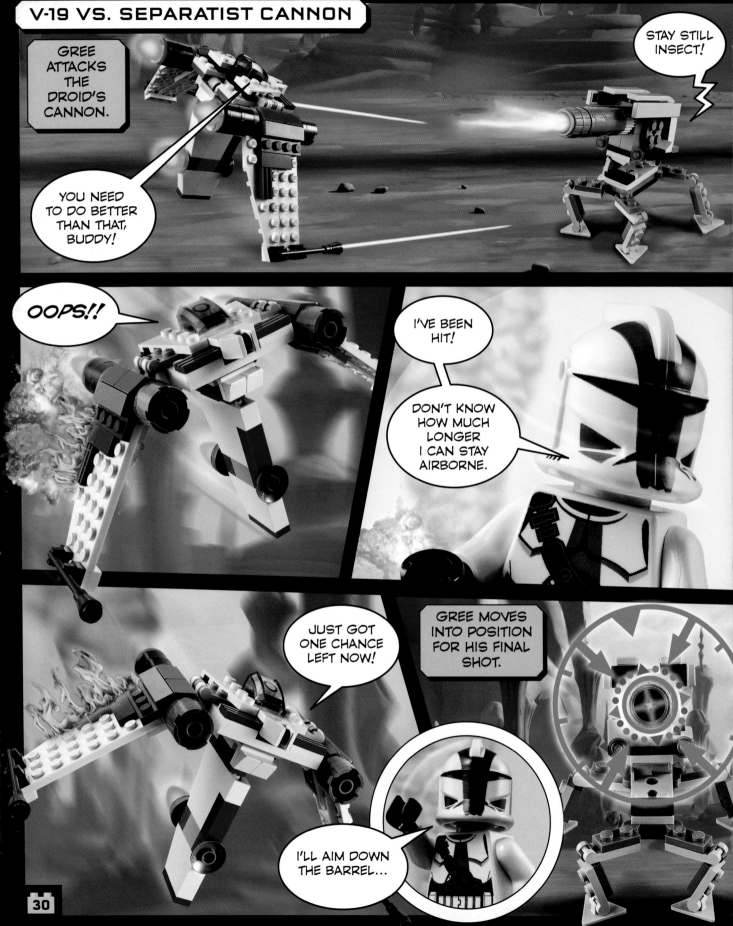

AMBUSH IN THE FOREST

WT-RT WALKER VS. VESPULA FIGHTER

HEADING INTO THE FOREST

GREE RECEIVES A HOLOTRANSMISSION UPDATE FROM MASTER YODA. THE DROID WITH THE STOLEN LIGHTSABER CRYSTALS HAS GONE INTO THE FOREST.

SPECIAL TRANSPORT NEED YOU WILL!

LOOKS LIKE I'LL HAVE TO USE THE BRICKS I'VE GOT.

LUCKILY I KNOW JUST WHAT TO BUILD...

LATER...

THIS WALKER WILL GET THROUGH ANY TERRAIN...

...WATCH OUT DROID. I'M AFTER YOU!

STOMP! STOMP! STOMP! STOMP!

NOW READ ABOUT THE **WT-RT WALKER** AND BUILD YOUR OWN. THE ADVENTURE CONTINUES ON **PAGE 42**.

WT-RT WALKER

The Wet Terrain Recon Transport is a Republic walker specially engineered for wet conditions such as swamps, marshes, and forests. The tall vehicle is manned by an individual clone trooper who has a raised view for patrols and reconnaissance missions. WT-RTs are also armed with multiple weapons for doing battle.

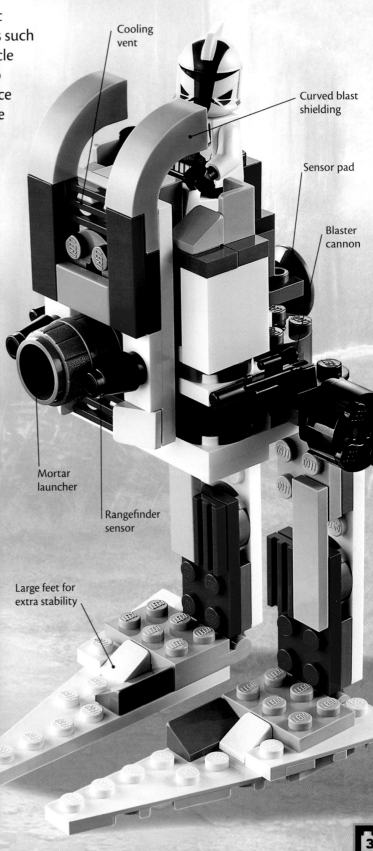

Cooling vent

Curved blast shielding

Sensor pad

Blaster cannon

Mortar launcher

Rangefinder sensor

Large feet for extra stability

WATERPROOF

The WT-RT has extra-wide feet to prevent sinking in wet ground, and is coated in a special non-rust finish. Two legs mean the walker is easy to maneuver in dense forest, but be warned: Two legs are less stable than four.

DATA FILE

NAME: Wet Terrain Recon Transport (WT-RT)
CLASS: Walker
TOP SPEED: 90 kph (56 mph)
ARMAMENT: Two blaster cannons, mortar launcher
ROLE: Reconnaissance, patrols, anti-infantry
CREW: One clone pilot/gunner
AFFILIATION: The Republic

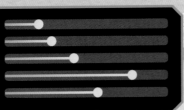

SPEED
RANGE
ARMOR
FIREPOWER
DEFENSE

WT-RT WALKER

The two-legged Wet Terrain Recon Transport is made up of five parts. First build the base for the clone pilot and its front panel. Next build each leg and foot and then assemble them together.

5

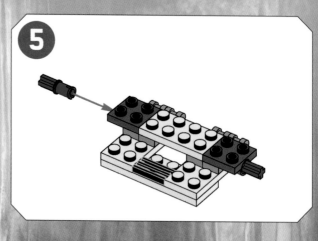

1

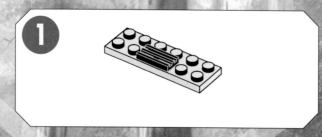

2

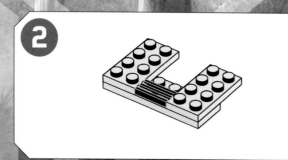

6

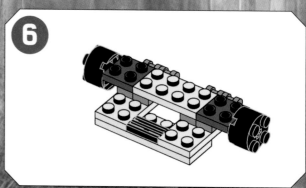

3

7

4

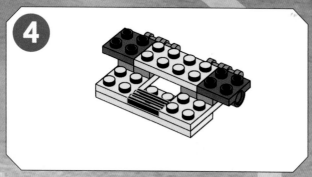

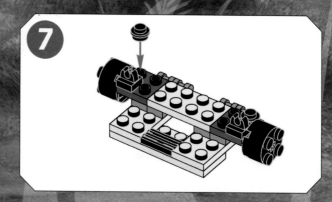

DID YOU KNOW?

The WT-RT is just one of many walkers used by the clone army. Some are small like the AT-RT (All Terrain Recon Transport) and some are large like the AT-TE (All Terrain Tactical Enforcer).

8

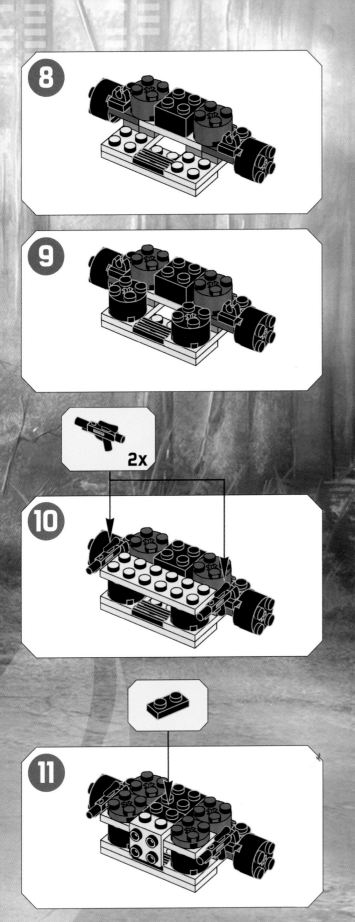

9

10

2x

11

12

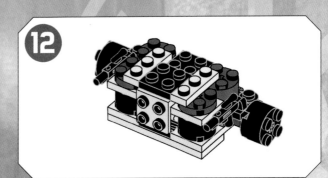

1 **2**

13

14

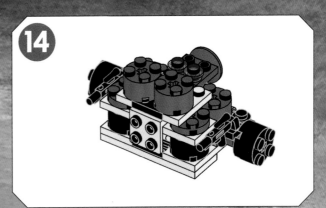

Turn the page to complete the model.

WT-RT WALKER CONTINUED

TOP TIP

Take your time with your building. Follow the instructions carefully and soon you'll be a LEGO brickmaster!

15

16
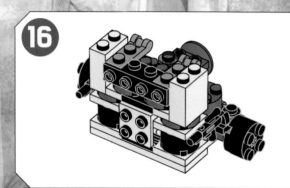

17
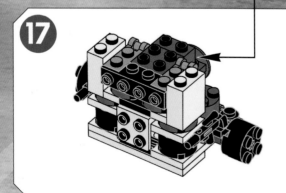

1
2
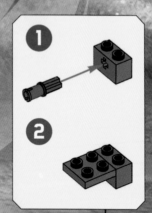

18
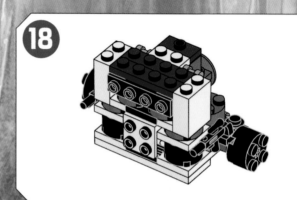

19

20
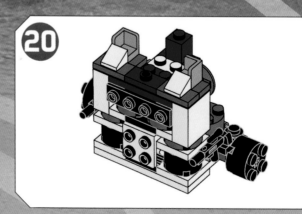

MORTAR LAUNCHER

1

2

3

4

5

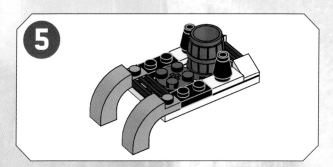

6

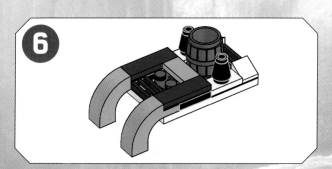

7

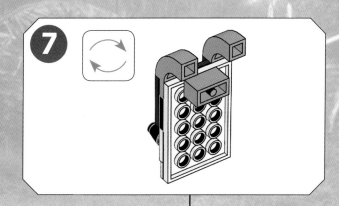

21

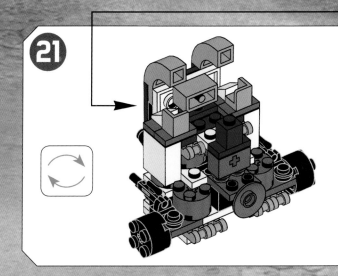

BOOM!

Turn the page
to complete
the model.

37

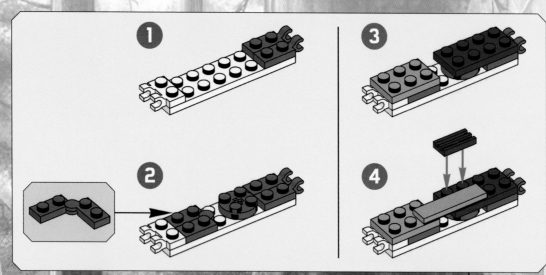

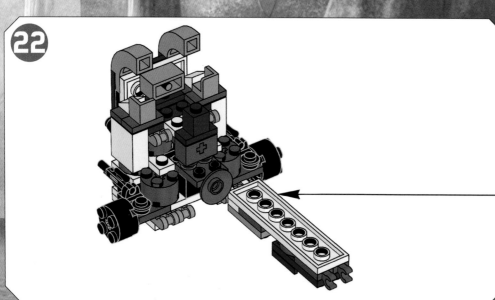

I MIGHT LOOK LIKE JANGO FETT, BUT I CAN THINK FOR MYSELF!

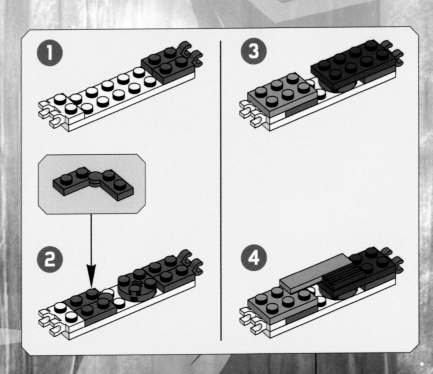

DON'T GET BOGGED DOWN!

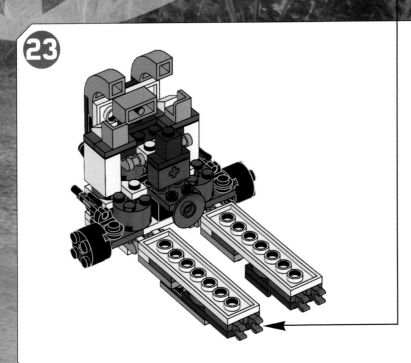

Turn the page to complete the model.

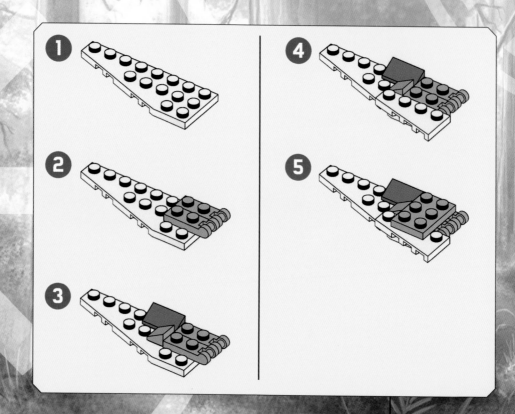

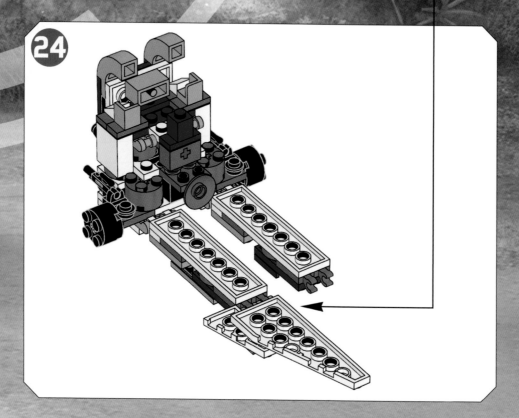

1

4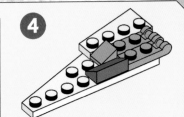

2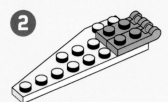

5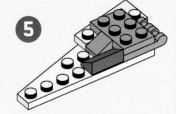

3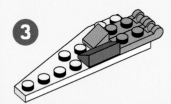

STOMP, STOMP, STOMP!

25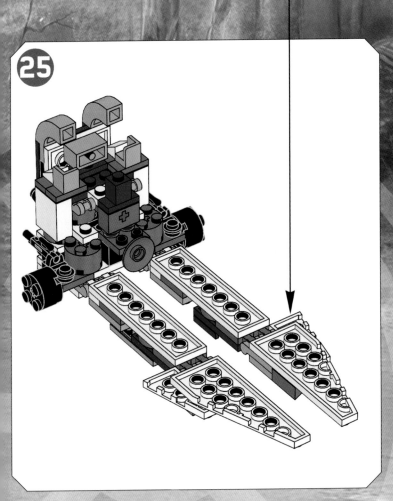

26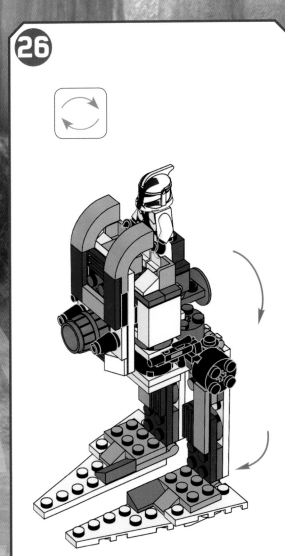

VESPULA FIGHTER

Swift, compact, and deadly, the Vespula gets up close to its target and strikes with the precision of a wasp. To keep the fighter light and nimble, it has little armor. For defense it relies on a pilot's skill to dodge enemy fire with acrobatic twists and turns.

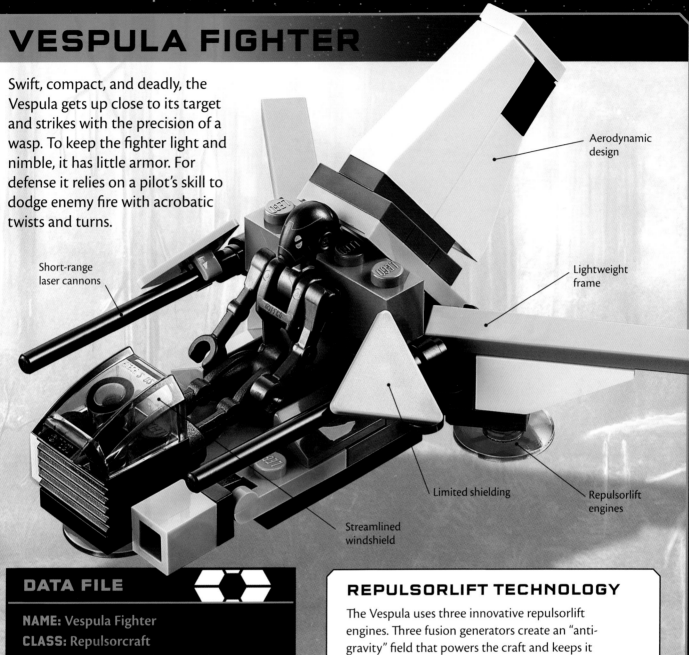

Aerodynamic design

Lightweight frame

Short-range laser cannons

Limited shielding

Repulsorlift engines

Streamlined windshield

DATA FILE

NAME: Vespula Fighter
CLASS: Repulsorcraft
TOP SPEED: 800 kph (500 mph)
ARMAMENT: Two laser cannons
ROLE: Head-on combat, attack
CREW: One droid pilot/gunner
AFFILIATION: The Separatists

SPEED
RANGE
ARMOR
FIREPOWER
DEFENSE

REPULSORLIFT TECHNOLOGY

The Vespula uses three innovative repulsorlift engines. Three fusion generators create an "anti-gravity" field that powers the craft and keeps it hovering above the ground.

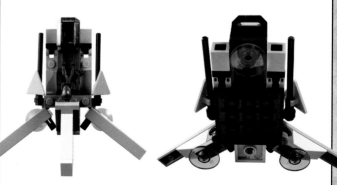

FROM ABOVE

FROM BELOW

VESPULA FIGHTER

This compact Separatist craft is made in two stages: first the hull and wings and then the dorsal fin. The wings and back section are hinged and there are two deflector shields that can also be repositioned.

TOP TIP

Hinged LEGO pieces can be used to make all sorts of moveable models. Use your imagination to create your own models and stories with these bricks.

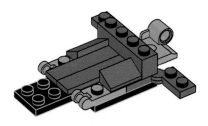

SURPRISE ATTACKER!

3x

2x

7

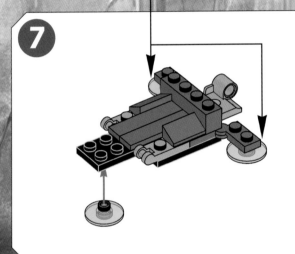

8

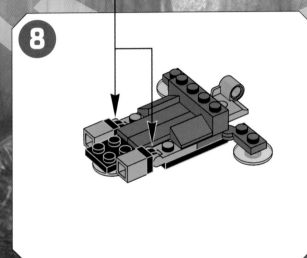

IT TAKES A SKILLED PILOT TO FLY THIS THING. AND THAT'S ME!

Turn the page to complete the model.

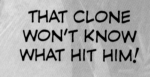

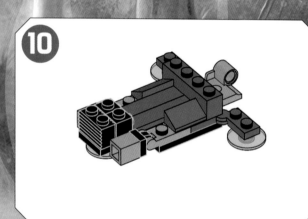

THAT CLONE WON'T KNOW WHAT HIT HIM!

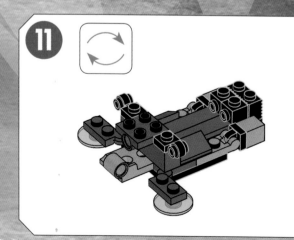

13

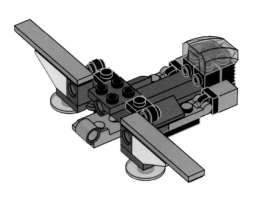

DID YOU KNOW?

Vespula is a genus of wasp. Like the wasp, the Vespula fighter buzzes up close to attack its victim and then makes a fast getaway.

14

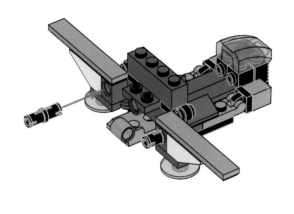

2x

15

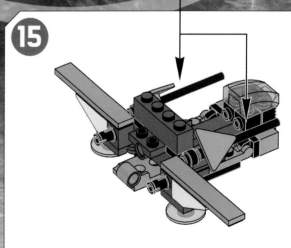

BZZZZZ!

Turn the page to complete the model.

VESPULA FIGHTER CONTINUED

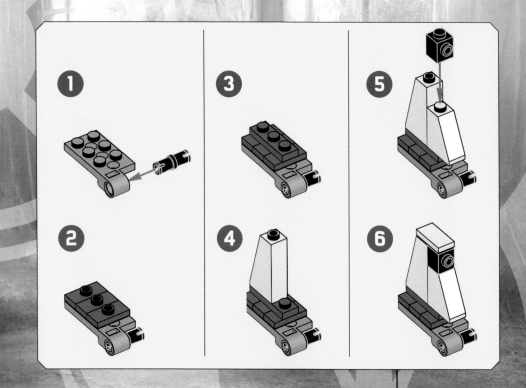

DESERT ATTACK

DESERT SPEEDER VS. PH-STAP

HEADING INTO THE DESERT

INCOMING MESSAGE FOR GREE...

ESCAPED AGAIN, THE DROID HAS. FLEEING ACROSS THE DESERT, HE IS. BUILD A NEW CRAFT, YOU MUST.

THIS BRICKMASTER TELLS ME EVERYTHING I NEED TO KNOW TO BUILD A NEW VEHICLE!

SOON...

I'LL JUST FIT THIS BLASTER ONTO THE SPEEDER.

THIS LANDSPEEDER WILL GET ME THERE IN TWO SHAKES OF JABBA THE HUTT'S TAIL.

GREE SPEEDS OFF TO THE DESERT...

I'LL GET OUR CRYSTALS BACK IN NO TIME!

NOW READ ABOUT THE **DESERT SPEEDER** AND BUILD YOUR OWN! THE ADVENTURE CONTINUES ON **PAGE 58**.

DESERT SPEEDER

The desert speeder is one of many types of landspeeder. It was designed using technology developed on the sandy planet Tatooine. Cooling systems prevent overheating, and filters stop sand from clogging up the engine. Long-range radar helps clone pilots navigate in sandstorms.

TRIPLE POWER

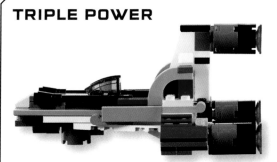

The desert speeder has three powerful turbine jet engines. Out in the open desert, where there are no obstacles to slow it down, the craft can really pick up speed.

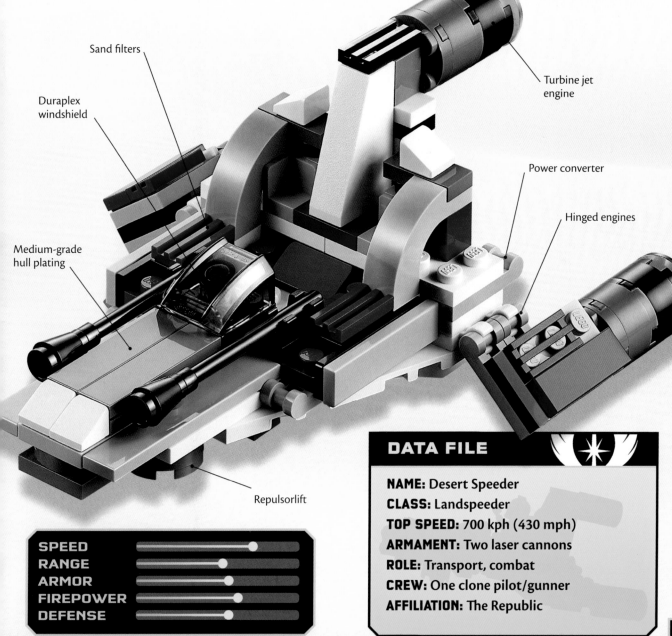

Sand filters

Duraplex windshield

Medium-grade hull plating

Turbine jet engine

Power converter

Hinged engines

Repulsorlift

SPEED
RANGE
ARMOR
FIREPOWER
DEFENSE

DATA FILE

NAME: Desert Speeder
CLASS: Landspeeder
TOP SPEED: 700 kph (430 mph)
ARMAMENT: Two laser cannons
ROLE: Transport, combat
CREW: One clone pilot/gunner
AFFILIATION: The Republic

DESERT SPEEDER

This modified landspeeder has a long nose, where the clone pilot sits, and three jet engines, two of which are hinged.

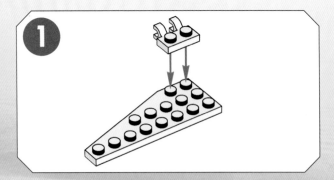

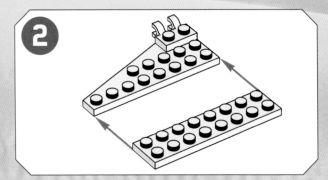

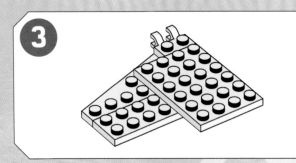

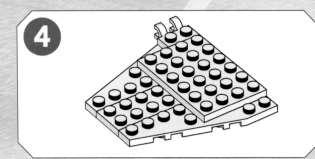

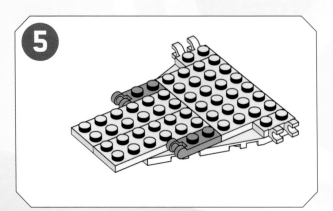

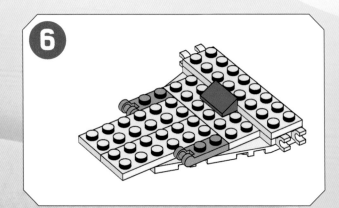

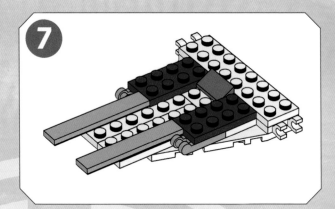

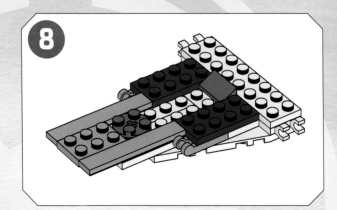

9

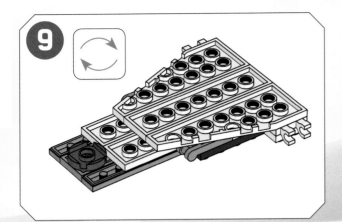

TOP TIP

Compare the pictures of each step, brick by brick, to make sure you haven't overlooked adding anything.

12

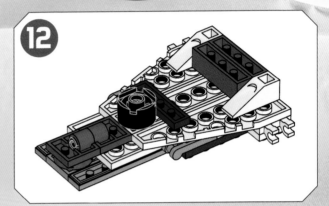

1

2

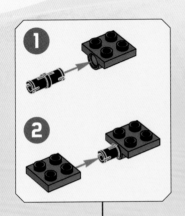

13

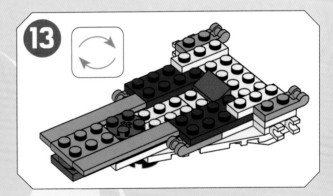

10

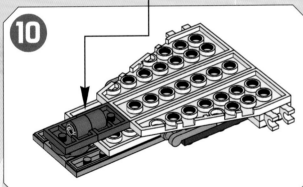

14

11

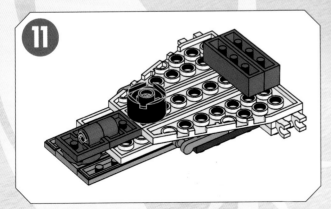

Turn the page to complete the model.

DESERT SPEEDER CONTINUED

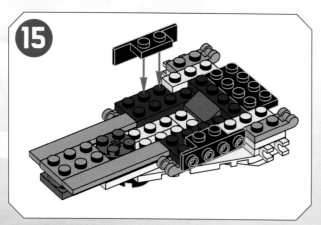

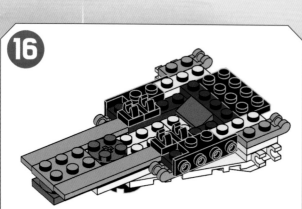

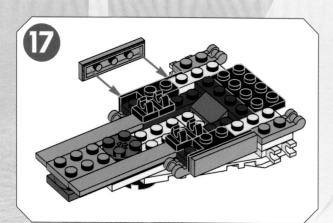

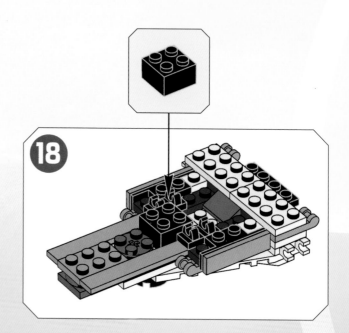

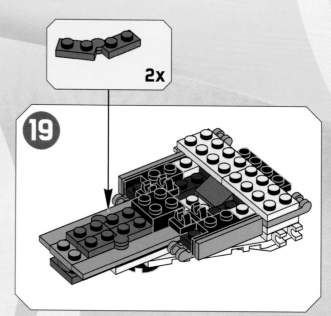

2x

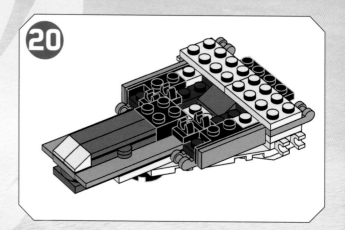

2x

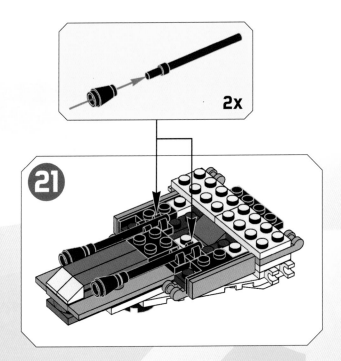

21

22

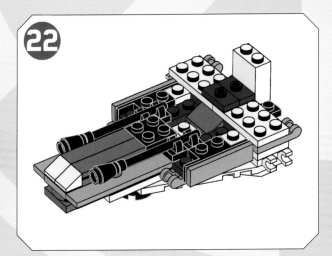

23

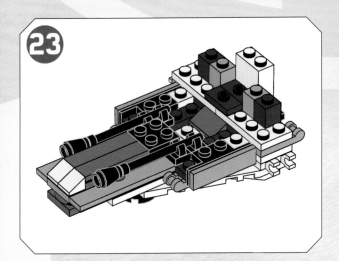

24

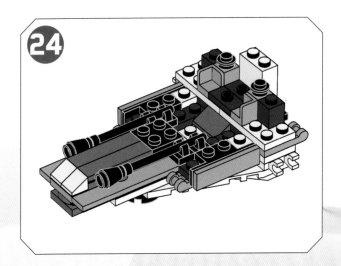

25

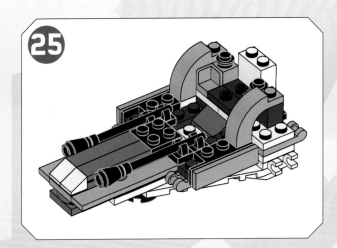

26

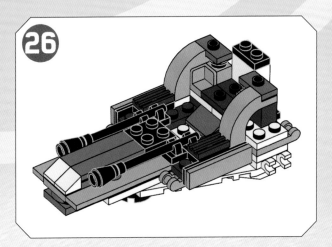

Turn the page
to complete
the model.

DESERT SPEEDER CONTINUED

27

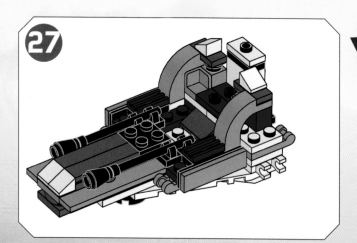

28

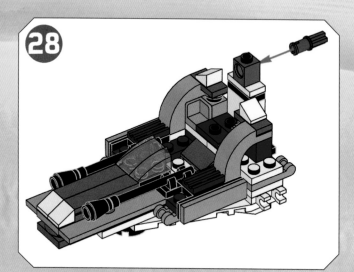

29

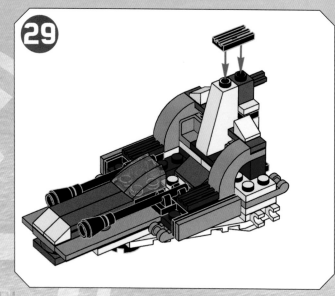

WHOOSH!

1

2

3

4

30

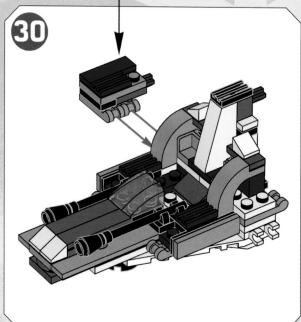

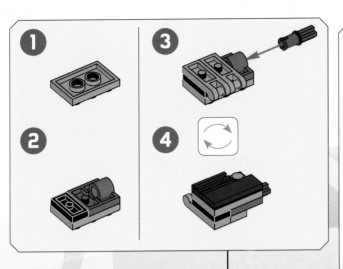

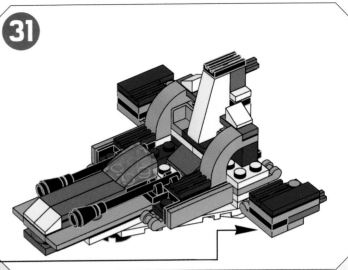

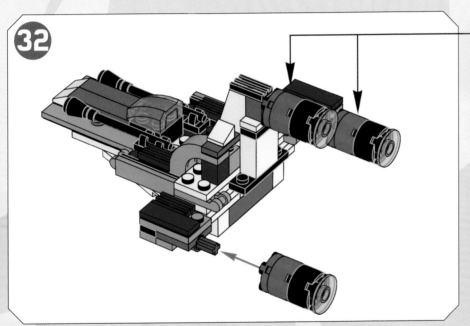

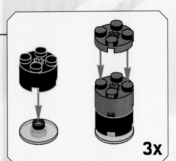

3x

GET READY
TO BE SCRAP
METAL, DROID!

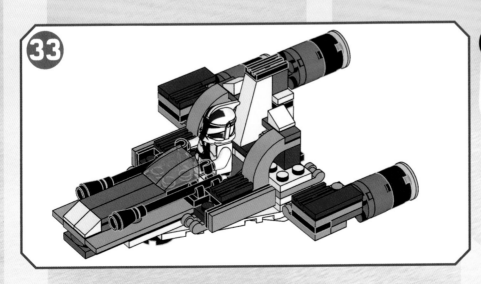

STAP ATTACK!

IN THE DESERT, THE DROID IS ALSO BUILDING A NEW VEHICLE...

ALMOST DONE!

THIS STAP HAS THE AGILITY AND FIREPOWER I NEED...

...TO FINISH THAT CLONE ONCE AND FOR ALL!

MEANWHILE, GREE SPOTS SOMETHING IN THE DESERT.

WHAT'S THAT IN THE DISTANCE?!?

YOU'D BETTER RUN, CLONE!

ZIPP!
ZIPP!
ZIPP!

GOT TO JUMP BACK IN MY SPEEDER!

BOOM!

NOW READ ABOUT THE **PH-STAP** AND BUILD YOUR OWN! THE ADVENTURE CONTINUES ON **PAGE 63**.

PH-STAP

The Phantom is a type of STAP (Single Trooper Aerial Platform) used by the Separatist army. It brings speed, firepower, and agility to the battlefield. Ph-STAP are small so are perfect for sneaking up on a target and destroying it before anyone can retaliate. Commander Gree had better watch out!

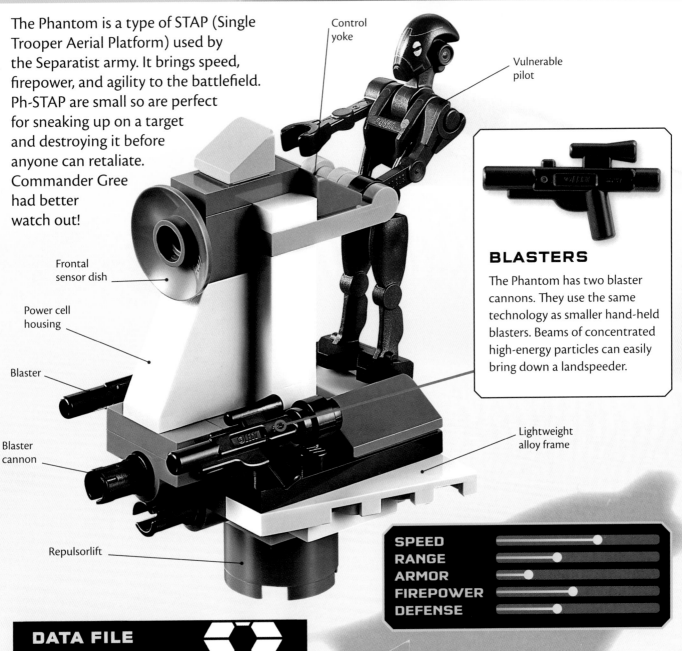

Control yoke

Vulnerable pilot

Frontal sensor dish

Power cell housing

Blaster

Blaster cannon

Repulsorlift

Lightweight alloy frame

BLASTERS

The Phantom has two blaster cannons. They use the same technology as smaller hand-held blasters. Beams of concentrated high-energy particles can easily bring down a landspeeder.

SPEED			
RANGE			
ARMOR			
FIREPOWER			
DEFENSE			

DATA FILE

NAME: Phantom Single Trooper Aerial Platform (Ph-STAP)
CLASS: STAP
TOP SPEED: 650 kph (400 mph)
ARMAMENT: Two blaster cannons
ROLE: Anti-infantry, reconaissance
CREW: One droid pilot/gunner
AFFILIATION: The Separatists

POWER CELL

The Phantom has a wider trunk than other STAPs so it is able to carry a larger energy cell. This powers the craft for longer, making it more reliable. In battle, this could make the difference between destruction and surviving to fight another day.

PH-STAP

The Phantom is one of many types of Single Trooper Aerial Platform. It is a tall, narrow craft with standing space for one droid pilot, and you can build it in a single stage.

TOP TIP

Be creative! Invent your own battles and stories using these vehicles and minifigures.

1

2
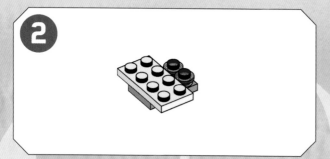

3
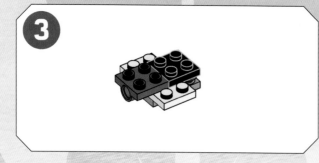

4
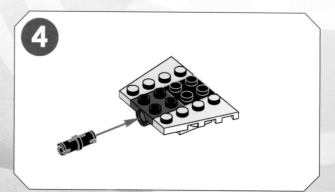

5
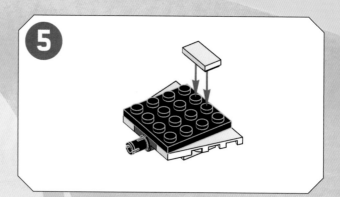

ROGER, ROGER!

6

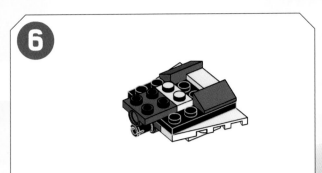

GET READY FOR ACTION!

7

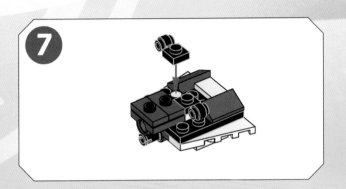

10

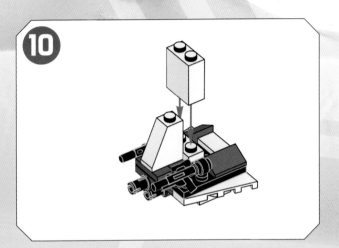

8

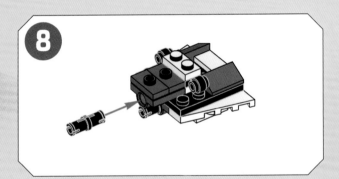

1 **2**

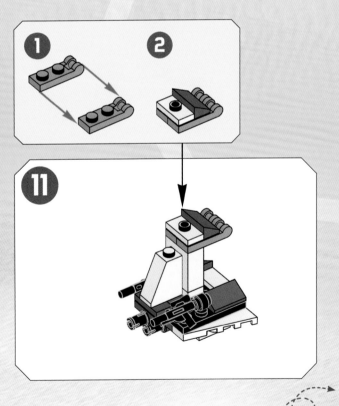

2x

9

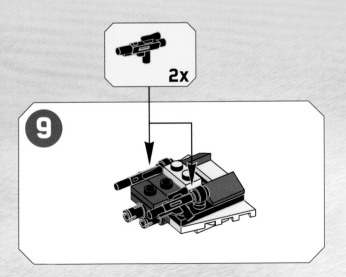

11

Turn the page to complete the model.

Turn the page
to complete
the model.

TOP TIP

Why not use your own LEGO bricks to make stands to display your vehicles on?

12

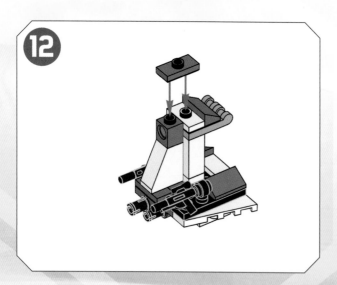

13

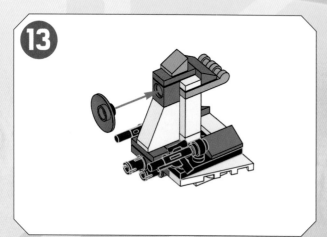

14

DID YOU KNOW?

Military STAPs used in battle by the Separatists evolved from the design of airhook speeders—a type of civilian craft.

15

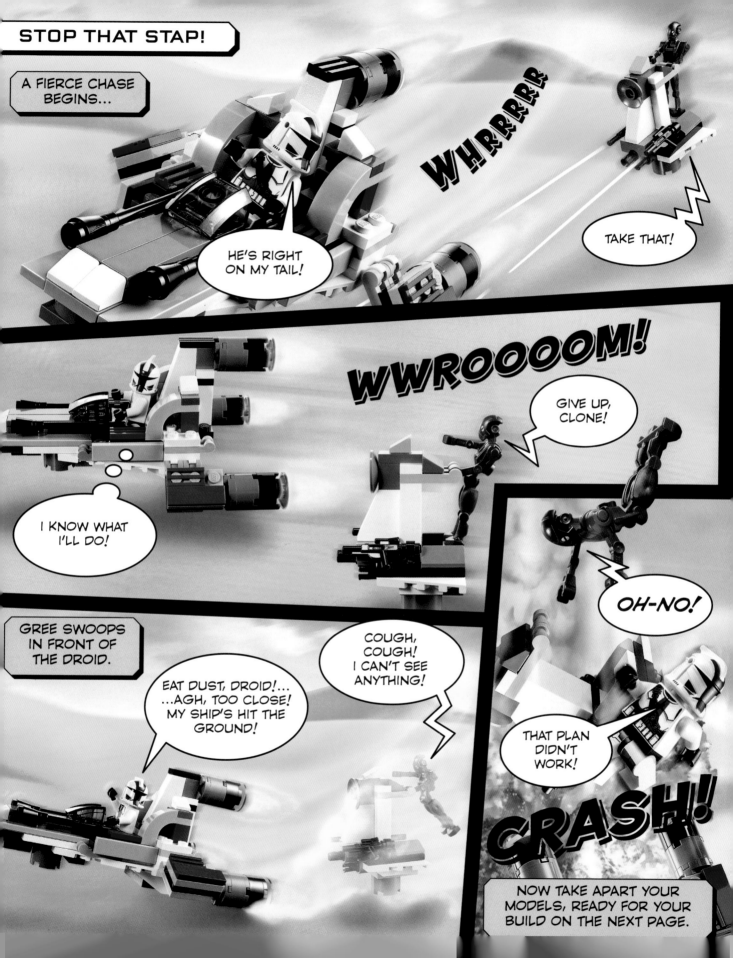

ICE MOUNTAIN CHASE

KD81 CARGO SKIFF VS. ICE SPEEDER

INTO THE ICE

WHILE GREE SORTS THROUGH THE WRECKAGE OF HIS SPEEDER, THE DROID SLIPS AWAY TO DIG UP THE CRYSTALS.

HA HA HA!

THAT CLONE DIDN'T STOP ME! SOON THE CRYSTALS WILL BE FAR, FAR AWAY!

THE DROID USES HIS BRICKS TO BUILD HIMSELF A CARGO SKIFF.

THE CRYSTALS WILL BE SAFE IN HERE!

TIME TO GET THESE LIGHTSABER CRYSTALS TO THE SECRET LAUNCH PAD!

THE DROID SETS OFF INTO THE ICE MOUNTAINS ON HIS NEW SKIFF.

WHOOSH

NOW READ ABOUT THE **CARGO SKIFF** AND BUILD YOUR OWN! THE ADVENTURE CONTINUES ON **PAGE 70**.

KD81 CARGO SKIFF

This droid vehicle is a smaller version of the gigantic freighters that criss-cross the galaxy. The skiff is perfect for transporting cargo over land, but it cannot travel into space. Although not designed for combat, it can still put up a good fight thanks to its blaster cannon, fitted to protect against pirate attacks.

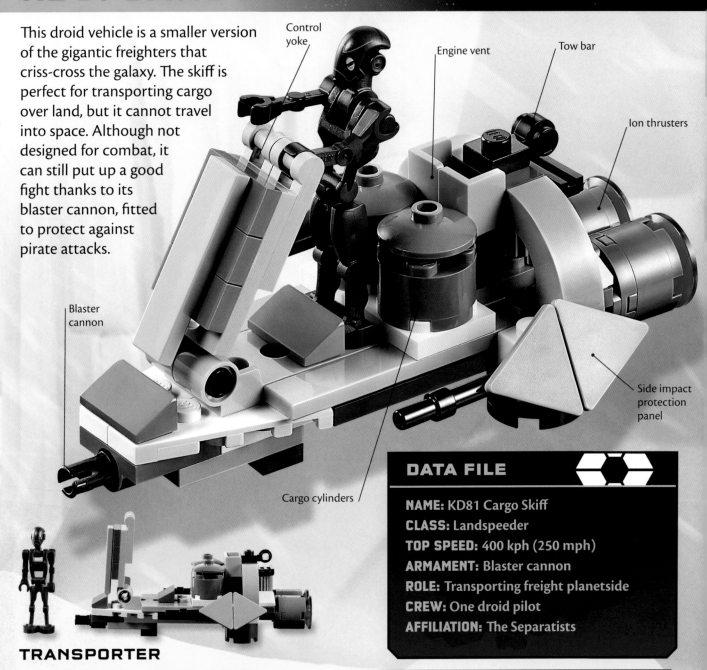

Control yoke

Engine vent

Tow bar

Ion thrusters

Blaster cannon

Side impact protection panel

Cargo cylinders

DATA FILE

NAME: KD81 Cargo Skiff
CLASS: Landspeeder
TOP SPEED: 400 kph (250 mph)
ARMAMENT: Blaster cannon
ROLE: Transporting freight planetside
CREW: One droid pilot
AFFILIATION: The Separatists

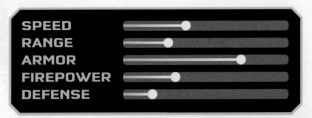

TRANSPORTER

The cargo skiff has a low centre of gravity and a long, flat base to make it as stable as possible. Room for the single pilot is small to maximize space in the hold.

SPEED	
RANGE	
ARMOR	
FIREPOWER	
DEFENSE	

CARGO

Magnetically sealed lid

These blast-proof containers are very plain and give no clue about their contents. They could be carrying anything from mundane spare parts for mining droids to smuggled spice, or stolen lightsaber crystals...

KD81 CARGO SKIFF

This vehicle for carrying goods has two storage containers. It is piloted by a single droid who stands up. The control yoke hinges backward and forward to allow the droid access.

1

2

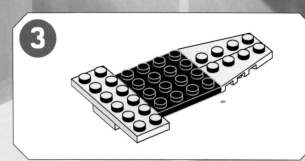

3

4

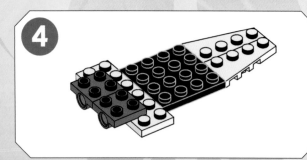

5

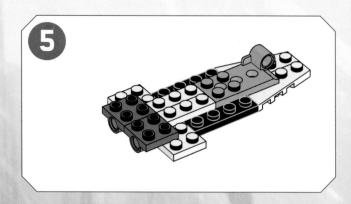

6

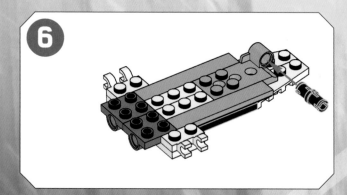

7

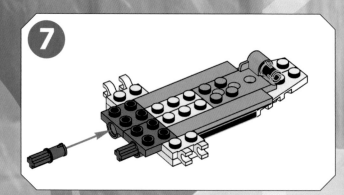

I'LL GET THIS BUILT IN A JIFFY!

8

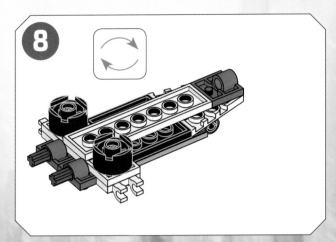

TOP TIP
Collect all the smallest LEGO pieces together and put them on a sheet of white paper. This will make them easier to find and sort.

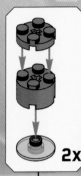

2x

9

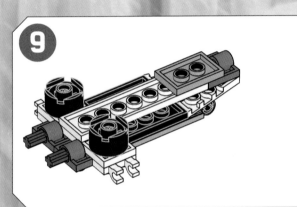

11

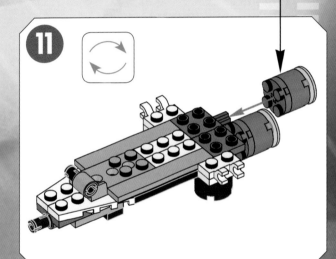

10

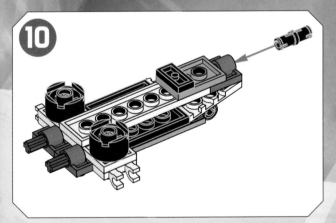

12

BLAST OFF!

Turn the page to complete the model.

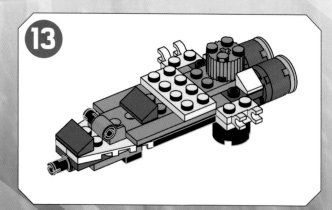

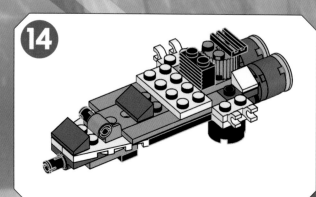

MY PRECIOUS
CARGO WILL BE
SAFE IN HERE!

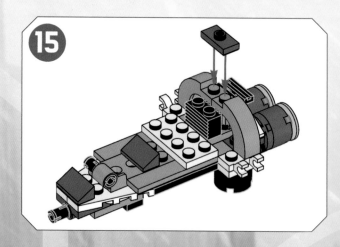

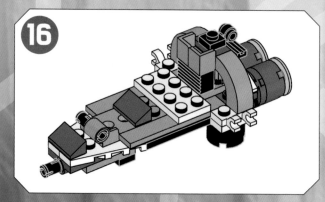

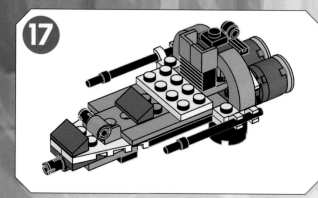

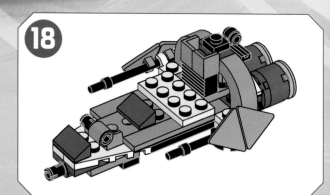

LET'S GO!

1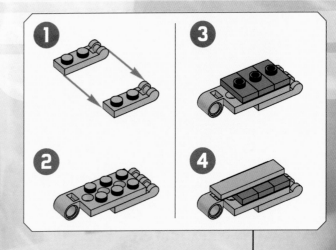

2

3

4

19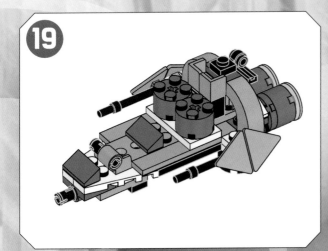

20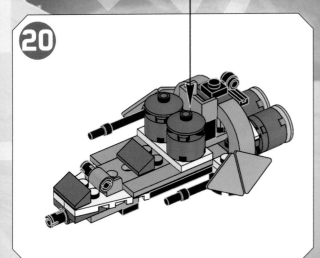

2x

21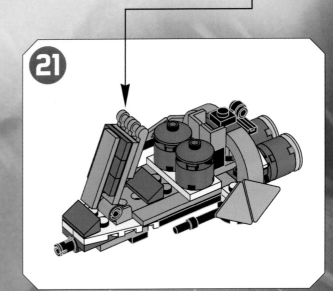

22

ICE SPEEDER

Frozen engines, cracked windshields, and fingers stuck to the controls are problems of the past in this airspeeder. It has been adapted for cold-weather missions with good insulation, under-panel heating, and the latest technology for keeping the engine free of ice particles. Plus, should a clone pilot get lost in a snowstorm, the long-range radar will see him home.

TRACTOR BEAM

A tractor beam uses a force field to lock onto and move objects. It is used for rescuing stranded crew, guiding incoming craft, capturing enemies, or even retrieving stolen property.

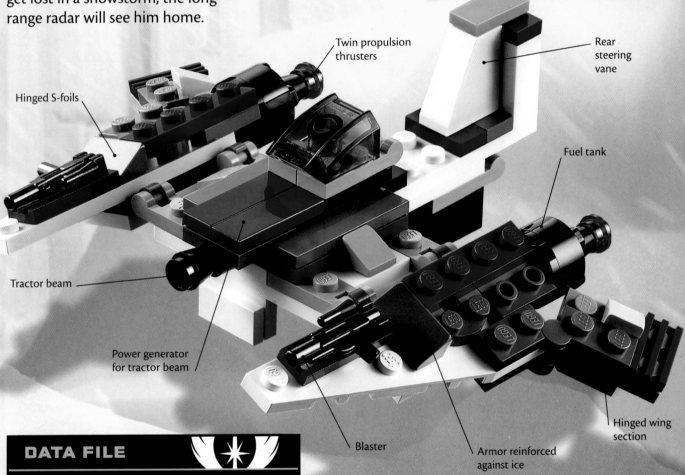

Hinged S-foils

Twin propulsion thrusters

Rear steering vane

Fuel tank

Tractor beam

Power generator for tractor beam

Blaster

Armor reinforced against ice

Hinged wing section

DATA FILE

NAME: Ice Speeder
CLASS: Airspeeder
TOP SPEED: 800 kph (500 mph)
ARMAMENT: Two blaster cannons
ROLE: Transport, combat
CREW: One clone pilot/gunner
AFFILIATION: The Republic

SPEED
RANGE
ARMOR
FIREPOWER
DEFENSE

ICE SPEEDER

This variation of a speeder is assembled from three parts: the main body of the vehicle where the clone sits and two hinged wings. Each wing also has a smaller hinged section.

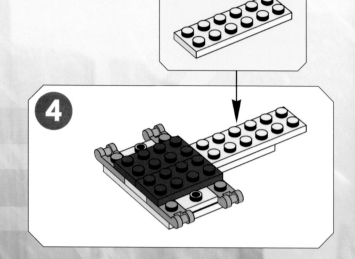

1

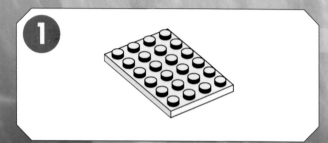

4

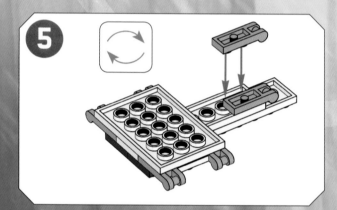

2

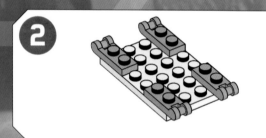

5

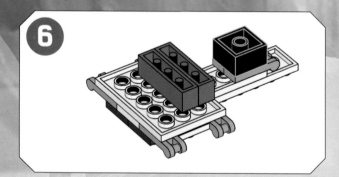

3

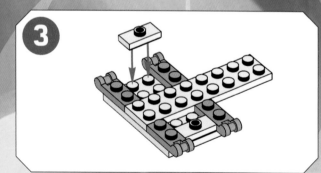

6

7

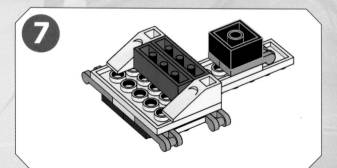

BRRR!

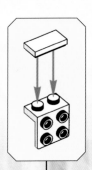

8

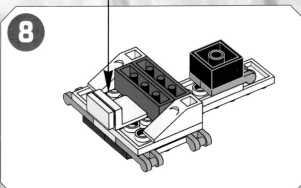

9

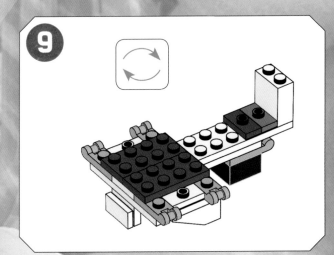

10

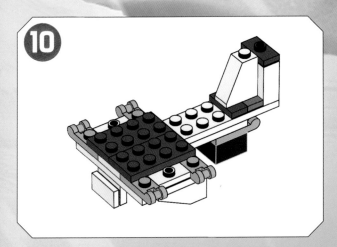

11

12

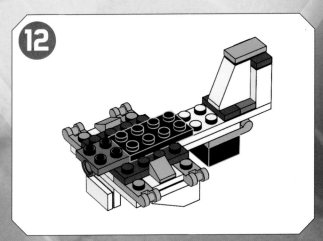

13

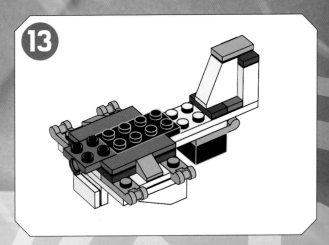

Turn the page
to complete
the model.

RIGHT WING

14

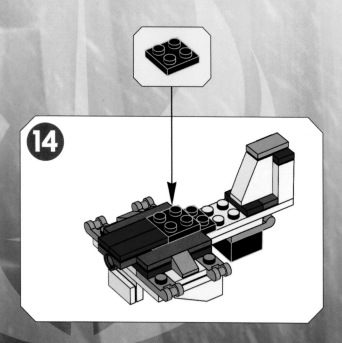

1

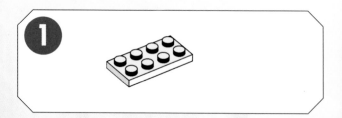

2

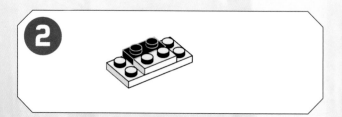

15

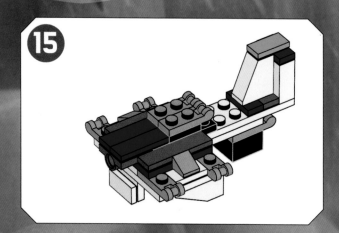

3

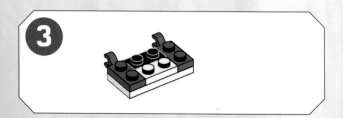

4

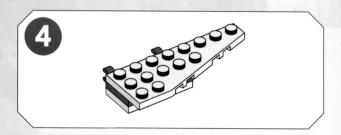

16

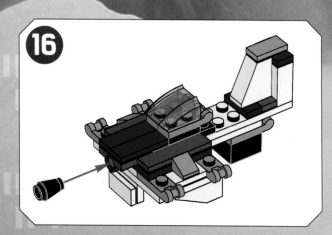

5

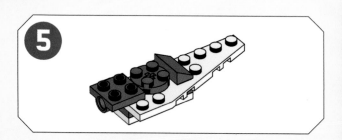

6

7

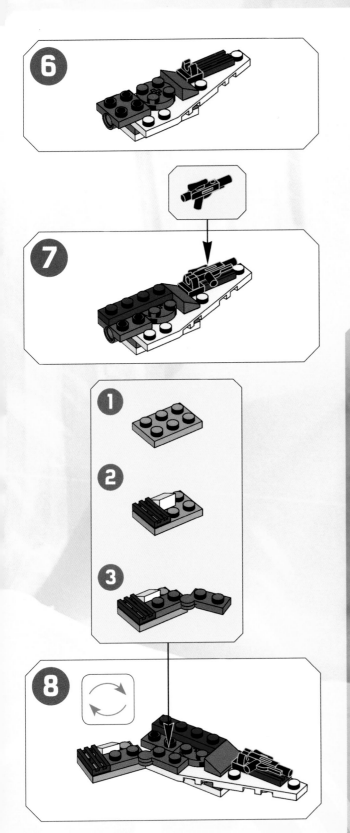

1

2

3

8

9

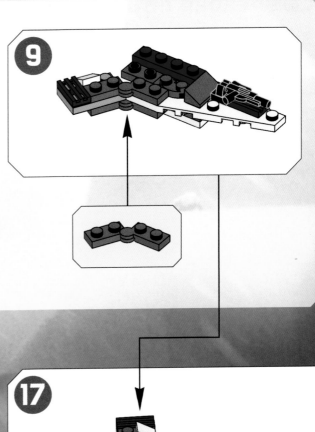

17

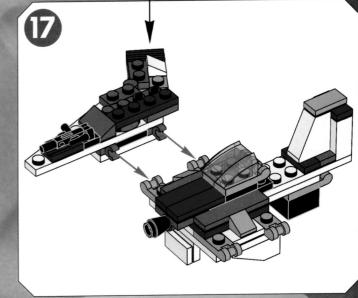

Turn the page to complete the model.

LEFT WING

1

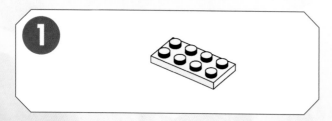

2

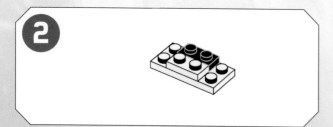

3

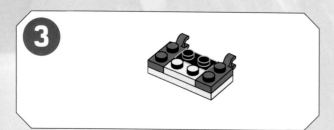

4

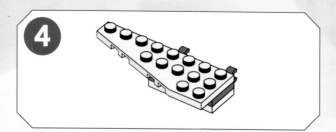

5

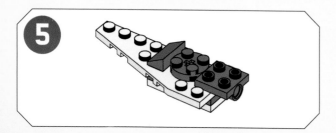

6

7

8

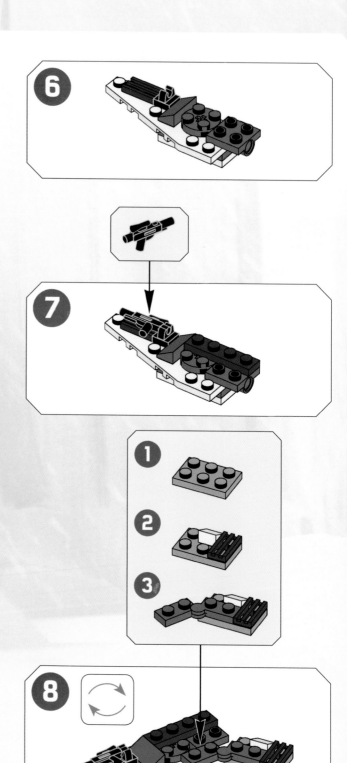

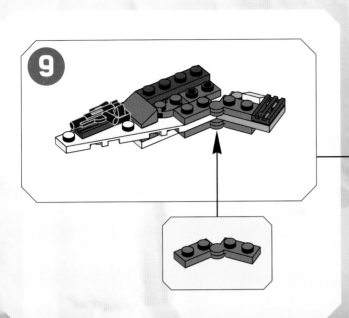

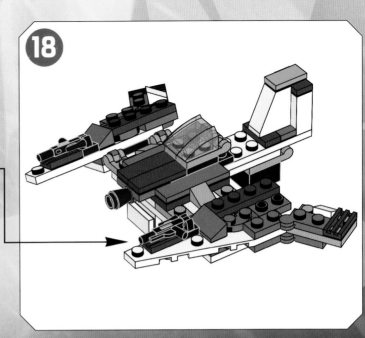

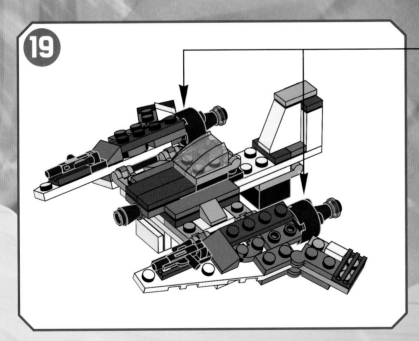

IT WILL BE
WARM AND COZY
IN THERE!

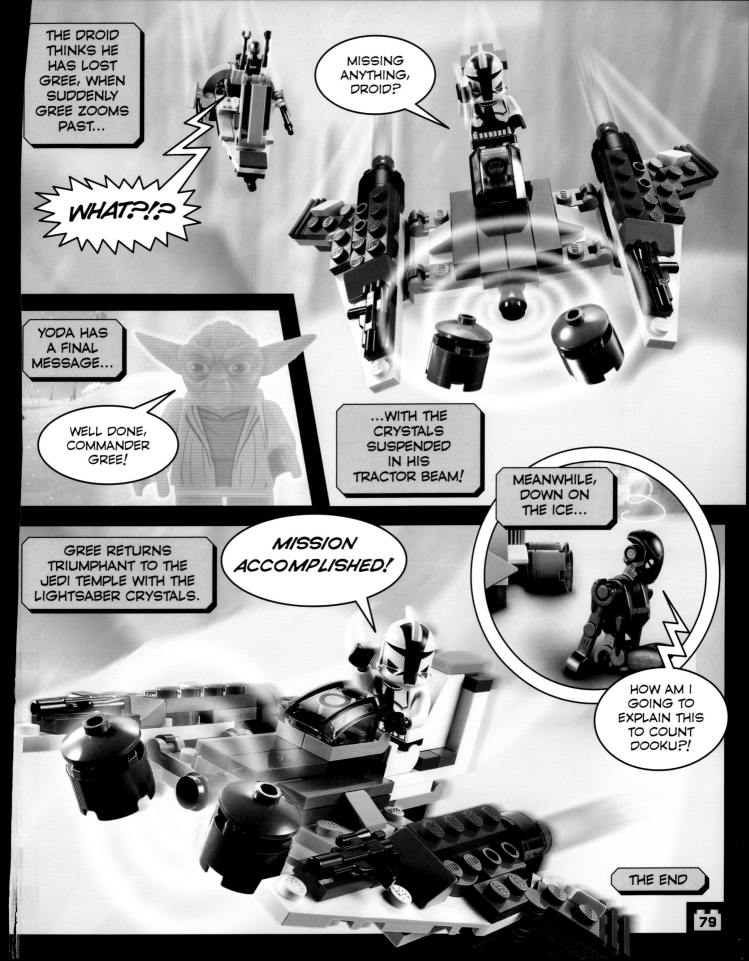

USE YOUR EXTRA IDEAS OWN BRICKS

You have built the models and played out the story, but the adventure is far from over! Why not use the bricks you have at home to add a surprise twist or start a whole new chapter? Here are some ideas to get you started.

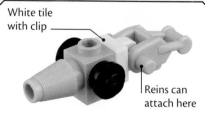

White tile with clip

Reins can attach here

A simple 1x2 tan brick and a tan cone form the eopie's head. Black 1x1 round plates on with side give the eopie eyes.

BUILD A EOPIE

Qui-Gon's ship is damaged when he is forced to perform an emergency landing on Tatooine. With Anakin's help, he has aquired a new hyperdrive—now he just needs to get it back to his ship! Build Qui-Gon a hardy eopie that can carry him through the hot Tatooine desert.

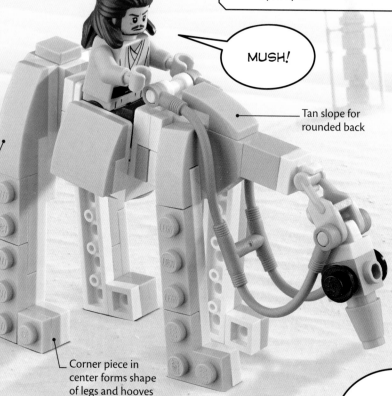

MUSH!

Tan slope for rounded back

Sloped piece attaches legs to main body

IN THE SADDLE

A space for Qui-Gon to sit is built into the eopie's body using inverted bracket pieces. These attach to its front and hind quarters.

Corner piece in center forms shape of legs and hooves

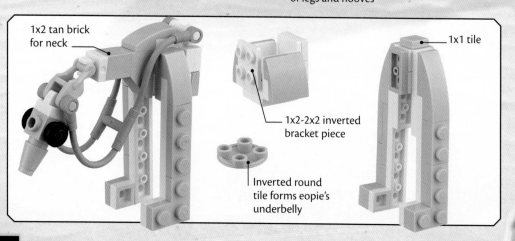

1x2 tan brick for neck

1x2-2x2 inverted bracket piece

Inverted round tile forms eopie's underbelly

1x1 tile

GOOD LUCK, QUI-GON!

BUILD AN ACKLAY

In the Geonosis arena, prisoners must battle execution beasts like this ferocious acklay with deadly claws and gnashing teeth. Will Obi-Wan, Padmé, and Anakin defeat the beast, or will they be gobbled up? Build an acklay and decide their fate!

Green tile

Handle piece attaches to body

Corner pieces are attached with tiles to form the long scaly acklay head.

2x2 corner plate

Angled bricks for scaly back

Angled bricks

Bricks with clip pieces for acklay's protective nodules

Sloped piece gives claw shape

ACKLAY BODY

Bricks with ball joints are built into the acklay's body so that the legs can attach. A clip at the neck attaches the head.

1x1 slope

2x2 brick with ball joint

Ball joint allows movement

I THINK I NEED TO CALL FOR SOME JEDI MASTERS!

For DK Publishing
Written and edited by Elizabeth Dowsett,
Laura Palosuo and Rosie Peet
Senior Designers Anna Formanek,
Nathan Martin, and Mark Penfound
Designer Stefan Georgiou
Pre-Production Producer Kavita Varma
Senior Producer Lloyd Robertson
Managing Editor Sadie Smith
Design Managers Guy Harvey and Victoria Short
Creative Manager Sarah Harland
Publisher Julie Ferris
Art Directors Lisa Lanzarini and Ron Stobbart
Publishing Director Simon Beecroft

For the LEGO Group
Project Manager Lars Jakobsen
Assistant Licensing Manager Randi Kirsten Sørensen
Senior Licensing Manager Corinna van Delden
Senior Design Manager Sine Klitgaard Møller
Associate Marketing Manager Louise Weiss Borup
Head Project Manager Torben Ebler Andersen
Designer Philip Kongsgaard Døssing
Building Instruction Developer Jean-Marc Lanoix-Warrer
Digital Photographer Brian Poulsen

Dorling Kindersley would also like to thank J.W. Rinzler, Troy
Alders, Leland Chee, and Carol Roeder at Lucasfilm Ltd;
and Tim Goddard for his amazing models.

First American Edition, 2018
Published in the United States by DK Publishing
345 Hudson Street, New York, New York 10014
DK, a Division of Penguin Random House LLC

Contains content previously published in LEGO® Star Wars™ Battle
for the Stolen Crystals (2013)

001—312752—July/18

A catalog record for this book is available
from the Library of Congress.

ISBN: 978-1-4654-8042-2

Printed and bound in China

www.dk.com
www.LEGO.com

A WORLD OF IDEAS:
SEE ALL THERE IS TO KNOW

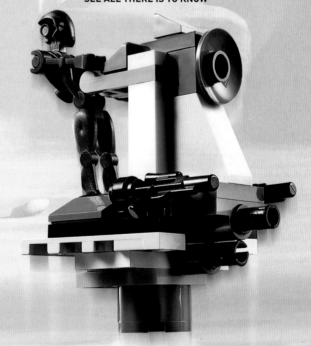